Thomas' Train

The Rev. W. Awdry
Illustrated by Robin Davies

Thomas often grumbled because he was not allowed to pull passenger trains. The other engines laughed. "You're too impatient," they said. "You'd be sure to leave something behind!" "Rubbish," said Thomas, crossly. "You just wait, I'll show you."

One night, Thomas and Henry were alone. Henry was ill.
The men worked hard, but he didn't get any better.

Henry usually pulled the first train in the morning, and Thomas would always get his coaches ready. He would fetch them from the Yard and bring them to the platform. "If Henry is ill," thought Thomas, "perhaps I shall pull his train."

In the morning Thomas ran to find the coaches.
"Come *along*. Come *along*," he fussed.
"There's plenty of time, there's plenty of time," grumbled
the coaches.

Thomas took them to the platform, and wanted to run round in
front at once. But his Driver wouldn't let him.
"Don't be impatient, Thomas," he said.

So Thomas waited and waited. The people got in, the Guard and the Stationmaster walked up and down, the porters banged the doors, and still Henry didn't come. Thomas got more and more excited every minute.

"What's the matter?" asked The Fat Controller.
The Stationmaster told him about Henry.
"Find another engine," The Fat Controller ordered, hurrying out
to the platform.
"There is only Thomas," said the Stationmaster.

"Thomas, you'll have to do it," said The Fat Controller. "Be quick now!" So Thomas ran round to the front and backed down on the coaches ready to start.

"Don't be impatient, Thomas," said his Driver. "Wait until everything is ready." But Thomas was too excited to listen to a word he said.

Nobody knows what happened next. Perhaps they forgot to couple Thomas to the train. Perhaps Thomas was too impatient to wait until they were ready. Or perhaps his Driver pulled the lever by mistake.

But somehow, Thomas started. People waved and shouted at him but he didn't stop.

"They're waving because I'm such a splendid engine," Thomas thought importantly. "Henry says it's hard to pull trains, but I think it's easy."

"Hurry! Hurry! Hurry!" puffed Thomas, pretending to be like Gordon.
As he passed the first signal box, Thomas saw the Signalmen waving
and shouting at him. "They're pleased to see me," he thought.
"They've never seen me pulling a train before," and he whistled back
to them, "Peep, peep."

But soon Thomas came to a Danger signal.
"Bother!" he thought. "I must stop. And I was going so
nicely too. What a nuisance signals are!" And he blew
an angry "Peep, peep," on his whistle.

One of the Signalmen came running up.
"Thomas!" he said. "What are you doing here?"

"I'm pulling a train," said Thomas proudly. "Can't you see?"
"Where are your coaches then?" asked the Signalman.
Thomas looked back. "Why bless me," he said, "if we haven't left them behind!"
"Yes," said the Signalman, "you'd better go back and fetch them."
Poor Thomas was so sad, he nearly cried.

At the station all the passengers were talking at once. They were telling The Fat Controller, the Stationmaster and the Guard what a bad railway it was. Suddenly, they saw Thomas coming back into the station, looking very sad. When everyone saw how sad and sorry he was, they couldn't be cross any more.

So they coupled Thomas to the train, and this time he *really* pulled it.

Thomas worked very hard all day long, and he wasn't impatient at all.

"You've been a Very Useful Engine," said his Driver. "Well done."

But for a long time afterwards the other engines laughed at Thomas. "Look!" they said, "There's Thomas, who wanted to pull a train, but forgot about the coaches!"